Double Play

by Jesse McDermott

illustrated by Albert Lorenz

PEARSON

Scott
Foresman

Editorial Offices: Glenview, Illinois • Parsippany, New Jersey • New York, New York
Sales Offices: Needham, Massachusetts • Duluth, Georgia • Glenview, Illinois
Coppell, Texas • Ontario, California • Mesa, Arizona

CONTENTS

Chapter 1

Friday Morning

"Bye, Mom," Bill Harrison called over his shoulder as he was leaving his house. "Bye, Chester," he called to his dog. "See you after school!"

"Bill, wait!" his mother said. "You forgot your lunch!" She handed him the brown bag he had left behind.

"Thanks, Mom!"

Outside, Bill tucked the bag into his backpack and zipped up his jacket. Though May was half over, it felt like March.

In a few minutes he was walking by the park. Bill and his friends played war there a couple of times, crawling on their bellies around the big bushes. That was fun!

It was Friday, and Bill was looking forward to the weekend. With Little League tryouts only a week away, he was going to practice pitching and hitting with his dad. Last year Bill's team won the local championship. But younger players like Bill didn't get on the field very much. This year would be different, he promised himself. He had been practicing with his father since the beginning of spring.

Bill's friend Rob was waiting where he always did, at the stop sign at the busy intersection near his house. Lost in thought, Bill walked right past Rob and the stop sign.

"Hey, Bill!" Rob called to him. "Watch out!"

Bill had one foot on the curb and one in the street. A blue van whipped past him, and he jumped back on the sidewalk.

"Phew, that was close. Thanks, Rob!"

"No problem," Rob replied. "What were you thinking about?"

"Little League tryouts. What else?"

"Right now, there's nothing else," Rob said. "I really want to make the majors this year."

"Me, too. My dad's been practicing with me, so I feel pretty good about it."

Little League had two divisions. Rob and Bill had played in the minors last year. The older boys usually played in the majors, where players were allowed to steal bases. Both boys were ten-and-a-half years old. They would be a little embarrassed if they didn't make the majors this year.

They chatted about batting averages while waiting for their friend Craig to show up. Soon Craig came running into view. He slowed to a walk when he spotted Bill and Rob and was panting when he reached them.

"Hi, guys," he said. "I bet you were early."

"Actually, I was," Rob said. "But it doesn't matter. We're not late."

The ten-minute walk to school took the boys along several blocks of tree-lined streets.

Near Ms. Snippley's yard, the chop-chop-chop of an old-fashioned lawn mower turned their heads. A big, bald man was pushing it. He had a long, gray beard that made him seem out of place in the neighborhood. His lawn mower looked like a giant pencil sharpener on wheels.

"My mom says he's crazy," Rob said as they sneaked through Ms. Snippley's yard.

"Crazy how?" asked Bill.

"Well, like that," Rob said. He nodded toward the man, who was now walking backwards and pushing the lawn mower behind him.

"Sometimes people say hello, and he doesn't even look at them," Craig chimed in. "My dad says it's because he's sick."

He seemed pretty healthy to Bill. In fact, he looked as strong as the motorcycle sitting outside his garage.

The boys slipped through Ms. Snippley's yard and across an apartment building parking lot. They reached school about ten minutes before the bell.

Chapter 2

The Research Paper

Behind the school, some kids were playing soccer without a net, and a few of the sixth graders were tossing a football. Rob joined the soccer game. Bill and Craig walked over to some classmates who were discussing schoolwork. "Ms. Cunningham is going to give out the assignments today," said a red-haired girl named Susan Jones. "My brother did it last year and said it's all about research. Two kids in his class got Fs because they didn't do it right," she added.

"No way," said a boy. "She's too nice for that."

"It's true!" Susan insisted. "If you don't do it right, you don't get promoted to sixth grade."

Susan was the class worrier, and she was good at making others worry along with her. Bill didn't believe Ms. Cunningham would actually give anyone who worked hard an F in anything. She had a way of making sure everyone did his or her best. But her end-of-the-year assignment was famous for being really hard, and Bill had been dreading it all year.

A loud bell rang twice, and the students lined up by class at one end of the playground. A couple of Bill's classmates were still whispering about the upcoming assignment as they filed into the school. Bill was really nervous now. He wasn't a straight-A student, but he had never flunked anything. He didn't want to start now.

He made his way to Room 12 with the other fifth graders. Colorful posters lined the walls, and the windows looked out onto the playground. There were 25 desks set neatly in rows of five, each with a chair placed upside down on top.

Where was Ms. Cunningham?

She was always the first one there. The students put their chairs in place, sat down, and began talking. They talked quietly at first, then loud enough to fill the room with a dull roar. A paper airplane flew by Bill's seat in the third row and hit Susan in the back of the head.

Just then, the door flew open, and Ms. Cunningham raced into the room. "I'm sorry to keep you all waiting," she said as she plopped down a large canvas tote bag. "My car had trouble starting this morning."

Ms. Cunningham quickly hung her jacket on the back of her chair and walked around to the front of her desk. "Looks like everyone is here on time today except me," she said. "So there's no need to take attendance. Let's start right out with the research paper."

The class groaned, and Ms. Cunningham smiled. "People," she said, "you've got nine days to do this, and it's going to be fun because you're going to make it fun."

The students looked back at her, waiting to be convinced.

"Here's how it's going to work," Ms. Cunningham said. "A week from this coming Monday, each of you will give an oral report about an event in American history. I've chosen the topics and written each one on a slip of paper. The slips are in this bag," she said, holding up a grocery bag. "Now, after lunch today, we'll go to the library so you can find a book or two about your topic. That should be easy for you now, since we've just learned how to use the library for research, right?" The children nodded their heads.

Rob raised his hand. "Can we use the Internet?" he asked.

"Not this time," she answered. "I want you to learn how to research topics in books first. Books can't tell you everything, though, so I want each of you to ask your parents if they know anyone who experienced the event. That person can be a relative, a neighbor, or someone else you know. I want you to interview that person to get a first-hand report on the event—what it was like to be part of it."

"I want you to present your research in two parts. In the first part, you will tell us what you learned from books. In the second part, you will tell us what it was really like to be there."

A girl in the front row raised her hand.

"Yes, Rachael?"

"What if we can't find anyone who was there?" asked Rachael.

"Don't worry," Ms. Cunningham smiled. "Come to me. I'll help. Anything else? No? Okay, then, let's pick our topics."

One by one, the students went to the front of the class and drew a slip of paper from the grocery bag. When Bill's turn came, he plunged his hand to the bottom of the bag. There were several slips left. He settled on one and pulled it out. "The Vietnam War," he read aloud. "When was that?"

"Not so long ago, Bill," Ms. Cunningham said. "You shouldn't have any trouble finding someone to interview about that."

Chapter 3

Getting Interested in Vietnam

The class reviewed decimals for the next hour and spent another hour discussing a lesson on World War II. In that war, the United States helped defeat Germany, Italy, and Japan. *Who were U.S. troops fighting in Vietnam?* Bill wondered. *Why were they there?* He looked ahead to a chapter called "Conflict in Southeast Asia." The pictures of airplanes and soldiers looked interesting. *Maybe this won't be so bad after all,* he thought.

During the hour before lunch, the students discussed their assignments. Ms. Cunningham explained what she meant by interviews and how to make a list of questions to prepare for them. The more she talked, the more eager Bill was to get started on the assignment. The Vietnam War sure sounded a lot more interesting than some of the other topics.

The lunch bell rang, and the children lined up and walked quietly to the cafeteria. Bill sat with Rob and Craig and a few other friends.

"So, do you guys know anything about your topics?" asked Rob.

"Nope," said Craig.

"Nothing," replied Bill. "But I think the Vietnam War will be kind of neat. I mean, studying a real war sure beats playing war, and I get to talk to someone who's actually been in a real one."

"Yeah, you have a good topic," said Rob. "Want to trade?"

"What have you got?" Bill asked.

"A march that Martin Luther King led in Washington."

"Well, I'd like to know more about Martin Luther King," Bill said. "But I think I'll stay with the Vietnam War."

The boys passed the rest of lunch talking about other things, especially the coming Little League tryouts. When they got back to Room 12, Ms. Cunningham said, "Don't sit down. Just pick up a notebook and a pencil and follow me."

The students were soon scrolling through the library's database. Ms. Cunningham helped them find books and encyclopedias on their topics.

Bill found a book showing a helicopter flying over a jungle. *Cool,* he thought. Jets and helicopters fascinated him, so he began reading.

For the rest of the school day, Bill read about the war in Vietnam. He learned that Vietnam was divided into two parts in 1954. The Communists who ran North Vietnam wanted to rule all of Vietnam. The United States didn't want them to succeed. In 1961, President John F. Kennedy sent a few hundred U.S. troops to train soldiers in South Vietnam. The South Vietnamese couldn't defeat the Communist forces all alone. So in 1965, President Lyndon Johnson sent thousands of U.S. soldiers to back them up. Soon the United States was in an ugly war.

Bill read about some weapons that were used and some of the biggest battles. He learned that more than 50,000 Americans lost their lives in Vietnam.

Bill checked out the book and took it home. He finished it just before his mother called him to supper.

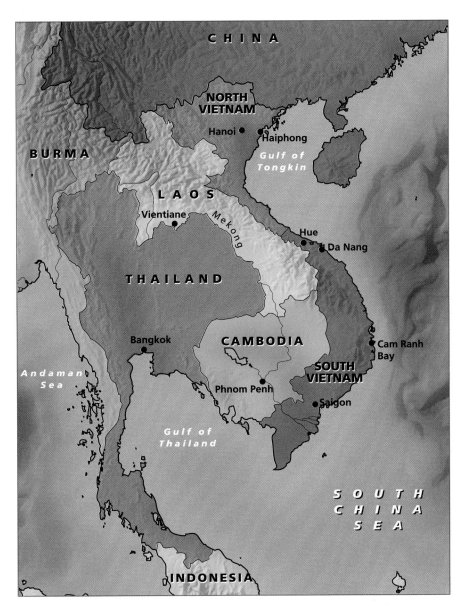

Vietnam was divided in two in 1954. Hanoi became the capital of North Vietnam. Saigon (now Ho Chi Minh City) became the capital of South Vietnam. After years of fierce fighting, the Communist government of North Vietnam got what it wanted in 1975. It defeated the South and brought both parts of the country under its control. The war took the lives of more than 2 million Vietnamese.

Chapter 4

Finding Out About Mr. Jenkins

Dinner in Bill's house always went the same. His parents would talk about their day, and then Bill would talk about his. But this time Bill was so excited about the assignment that he started talking as soon as he sat down.

"What have you learned about the war so far?" his father asked.

"A lot," Bill answered. "But I need to find out what it was really like to be there. Ms. Cunningham wants us to interview someone."

"That's interesting," his mother said. "Bob," she asked her husband, "do we know any Vietnam veterans?"

He pondered the question for a moment.

"What about Dan Jenkins? He's a veteran, and I think he was wounded there."

"That's right," Bill's mother said. "He's a very nice person."

"Who is he?" Bill asked. "Do I know him?"

"You probably pass his house on the way to school," his mother said. "He's got the best-kept yard on his block."

"And the best-kept beard, too," his father said. "We met him at the Davis's Fourth of July party last year. He had some hair on his head then, but last time I saw him he had shaved it all off."

"That guy?" Bill said. "I saw him today. . . . He seems kind of . . . well, weird."

"What makes you say that?" his mother asked.

"He was walking backwards and pushing this old-fashioned lawn mower behind him."

"It would be a pretty boring world if everybody did everything the same way," said his father.

"Well, Rob's mom thinks he's crazy, and Craig's dad said he was sick."

"Sick?" said Bill's father. "He looked pretty healthy when we met him at the party."

"Many soldiers came home with nightmares that haunted them day and night," Bill's mother said. "Maybe that's what Craig's father meant by 'sick.'"

"Oh, I see," said Bill, but he was still a little worried.

"We should really call Dan Jenkins and ask whether he'd be willing to be interviewed," said his mother. "A lot of veterans don't like to talk about Vietnam."

After dinner, Bill's father called Mr. Jenkins. "He said you can visit him anytime this weekend," he told Bill afterward. "Just call first to let him know you're coming."

Chapter 5

Talking to the Expert

When Bill woke up on Saturday morning, he glanced out the window. A mist was creeping over the front yard, and it was raining. The whole scene was eerie, like something out of a scary movie.

He fixed a bowl of cereal and flipped on the TV, changing channels until he found a weather report. When his parents awoke a little later, he knew the rain was going to last all day.

"We can't play ball in the rain," said his father. "Why don't you visit Dan Jenkins today?"

"Well, maybe." The prospect of learning more about the Vietnam War was attractive to Bill. But the prospect of spending time with Mr. Jenkins made him uneasy.

"Mr. Jenkins is a really nice man," said Bill's father. "C'mon, I'll call and see if he's free. If he is, I'll drive you over so you don't get soaked."

Mr. Jenkins was free, and around 11 o'clock, Bill and his father pulled up outside his house. Bill's dad walked with him up to the door, holding an umbrella over both of them.

"This must be Bill," Mr. Jenkins's voice boomed as he opened the door. Bill had forgotten how big he was. Mr. Jenkins towered over him.

"Hi, Dan," Bill's father said. "Yup, this is the young historian himself."

"He-hello," Bill stammered.

"Hello, there," Mr. Jenkins said. "Come on in out of the rain." He stepped aside to let Bill enter. "Bob, I've got some coffee on," he said.

"Thanks, Dan," said Bill's father. "But I've got a leaky faucet to fix." He handed the umbrella to Bill. "Bill, I'll see you at home. Dan, thanks a lot for taking the time to do this."

"I'm going to enjoy it," Mr. Jenkins said. "It's not every day that someone treats me like an expert."

"Why don't we sit in my study?" Mr. Jenkins said. He led the way to a large room. A desk sat in front of a picture window that opened onto the backyard. It was covered with papers, books, and a laptop computer and a printer. On the corner of the desk, a small glass vase held a few flowers that had withered days ago.

"Have a seat at the desk, Bill," said Mr. Jenkins. "You may want to take some notes." He moved a wooden armchair close to the desk, but did not sit down right away.

"Just give me a moment to find my spectacles," he said.

"Your what?" asked Bill.

"My spectacles. Eyeglasses, to help me see."

"We used that word when we studied Roman history," Bill said. "The Roman emperors used to put on spectacles like circuses to keep the people happy."

"Well, yes," Mr. Jenkins said. "That's another kind of spectacle. A lot of them were pretty bloody. Like Vietnam, in fact."

Mr. Jenkins located his glasses and put them on. "Now, then," he said, sitting down. Bill had just noticed that the walls were lined with books. "Have you read all these books?" Bill asked.

Mr. Jenkins chuckled. "Most of them, yes. You see, I'm a writer. And if I don't read, I don't have anything to write about."

"Do you write books?" Bill asked.

"I used to when I taught at the university," Mr. Jenkins said. "You wouldn't have liked them. I wrote them for other college teachers, and I'm sure many of those teachers didn't like the books, either." He smiled.

"Don't you teach anymore?" Bill asked.

"No," Mr. Jenkins replied. "My wife died, and . . . Well, that's another story. Do you like to read?"

"Sometimes," Bill said. "I mean, I like reading about exciting stuff. Sports, for instance, or fighter planes."

"What was the last book you read?"

"*The Wizard of Oz.* The book is sure better than the movie."

"Oh, I loved the Oz books," said Mr. Jenkins.

"You mean there are more?"

"There sure are. Twelve or thirteen more. In fact, I think I still have them on one of these shelves. . . ." Mr. Jenkins got up and walked over to a bookcase. "Ah-ha!" he said, pulling out a beaten-up paperback. He brought it over to Bill.

"Here you go. You can borrow this if you want to read it. I have the rest of the series here too."

Bill read the title, "*The Land of Oz.* Cool! Thank you, Mr. Jenkins!"

"You're welcome, Bill. But I don't think you came here because of all my books, did you?"

"No, sir, I didn't. I have to give this presentation in school about what it was like to be in Vietnam during the war. I have to interview someone who was there, and, well, you're it, and. . . ."

"Go ahead," Mr. Jenkins said, opening his eyes. "You can ask me anything you want to about 'Nam."

Chapter 6

Walking in 'Nam

"Why do you call it 'Nam?" Bill asked.

"That's soldier talk. Soldiers have their own names for things. We said 'VC' for Viet Cong, people in South Vietnam who fought for the Communists. The VC were farmers during the day and fighters at night. It was real hard to tell the good guys from the bad guys."

"When were you in Vietnam?"

"My first tour of duty was in 1968. Each tour lasted a year. I didn't stay in Vietnam for the whole tour, though. I got shot in the leg and landed in a hospital. When I got out, I signed up for a second tour."

"Why?"

"To get back at the guy who shot me, I guess. I was really mad."

"What was it like to be there?"

"I bet it sounds really cool, huh? Using real guns, the tanks, and helicopters and all?"

"Yeah, kind of."

"Well, the truth is, there's nothing worse than being in a real war. A real war means walking, walking, and more walking. We trudged through swamps and jungles, for weeks at a time. Jungles look real pretty from up above, but when you're down in them, sweating and swatting at bugs and sleeping in mud, things are very different."

Mr. Jenkins cleared his throat. "We moved slowly, because we had to watch every step. The North Vietnamese put traps and land mines everywhere, and you didn't want to step on one of those. We knew the enemy had the edge. It was their country, after all. They knew the jungle, how to blend in, where to find the best spot for an ambush."

"At night," Mr. Jenkins continued, "we dug trenches to sleep in. That's when the bugs became our biggest enemies. Bugs in Vietnam were like mosquitoes, only bigger and meaner. Severe rainstorms would make the ground so muddy you could sink in up to your shoulders, or worse. I'm not kidding."

"Yuck," Bill said, looking out the window at the falling sheets of rain.

"It wasn't a walk in the park, that's for sure, but I had my buddies with me, fellow Marines," Mr. Jenkins said. "When you're thrown into that, you become real close with the people around you. You depend on one another. You help one another get through it all. I made friends in 'Nam I'm still in touch with."

"How long did you spend in the jungle?" Bill asked.

"It depended on the mission. The longest I ever spent there was about a month. Back at the base, we got some rest when the VC weren't lobbing shells at us. We played cards, wrote letters home, and even managed to play a few games of baseball."

Bill's eyes lit up. "You played baseball?"

"Oh, sure. I was a pitcher at my high school, and I was pretty good. We had some good games in 'Nam, some good players."

"I love baseball," said Bill. "Tryouts for Little League are next week."

"No kidding?" Mr. Jenkins said. "What position do you play?"

"Last year I was a catcher, but I'd really like to be a pitcher. I've been practicing with my dad."

Mr. Jenkins smiled. "Don't be too quick to change positions," he said. "Without a good catcher, the pitcher is nothing. And you've got to be tough to be a catcher. It's good training for life."

"What do you mean?" Bill asked.

"Well," Mr. Jenkins replied, "I'll tell you a story about my grandfather. When he was a boy in Detroit, a guy named Ty Cobb played outfield there. Cobb was one of the greatest players ever. Before he retired in 1928, he made 4,191 hits and stole 892 bases. But he played a rough kind of baseball, and many players didn't appreciate that."

"You mean he'd hit people?"

"Not exactly," Mr. Jenkins said. "He liked to make the metal cleats on his shoes as sharp as daggers.

Then, if he got a chance, he would slide into home plate with one foot in the air. Catchers got out of his way pretty fast when they saw Cobb's cleats coming at them. He scored a lot of runs that way. But good catchers aren't so easy to scare. The quick ones learned how to tag Cobb with the ball without getting their legs cut up. Catching teaches you to be quick and tough."

"Did your grandfather know Ty Cobb?"

"He met him. Cobb was very superstitious. He thought it was bad luck to wear or even carry his baseball shoes into the ballpark. One day my grandfather tried to sneak into a game with some other kids and got caught. Well, who comes along but Ty Cobb. 'Here, kid,' Cobb said. 'Carry my shoes for me.' And so my grandfather got into the game after all, and Cobb stole three bases that day."

"Cool," Bill said.

"I think so too," Mr. Jenkins said.

Bill wanted to keep talking about baseball, but he figured he ought to ask more questions about Vietnam instead. Mr. Jenkins told him about visiting Vietnam with some other veterans in 1999. "We were shown around by guys who had fought against us 30 years before," he said. "That's when I realized how stupid wars can be. It's a lot easier to be someone's friend than it is to be an enemy."

Later, at home, Bill told his father everything he had learned about Mr. Jenkins. "It sounds like he's a baseball nut, just like us," his father said. "Maybe the three of us could go to a game together."

"I'd really like that," Bill replied. "When I take the Oz book back to him, can I ask him?"

"Absolutely," his father said.

Chapter 7

Making a Double Play

Bill spent the afternoon writing down what Mr. Jenkins had told him about Vietnam. On Sunday, the weather had cleared up, and he practiced pitching with his dad. Then Bill had his father pitch to him so that he could practice catching. His Dad was surprised. "What got you thinking about catching again?" he asked.

"Oh, just something Mr. Jenkins told me, I guess," Bill said.

The week passed quickly. Bill's regular homework kept him busy, but he continued to work on his oral report. He wrote down what he wanted to say and learned part of it by heart. He drew a large map of Vietnam and chose pictures from the library book to show the class. And every night before he went to sleep, he read a chapter of *The Land of Oz.*

On Saturday morning, Bill and his friends walked past Mr. Jenkins's house on their way to the tryouts. Bill held his mitt up and waved to Mr. Jenkins, who was working in his garden. Mr. Jenkins gave him a thumbs-up sign. "Good luck, soldier," he said.

"What were you doing?" Craig whispered when they were a few houses away. "You don't wave to a crazy man."

"He's not crazy," Bill responded. "He's the guy I interviewed for my report. He was a Marine, and he fought in Vietnam, and he's really a nice guy. He knows more about baseball than anyone I've ever met."

"Wow, really?" asked Rob. That changed everything.

"Yes, really," Bill said.

Bill had stopped worrying about the presentation. Thanks to Mr. Jenkins, he felt as prepared to give his report as he did trying out for the Little League majors.

He was right to be confident. On Monday, he gave his report. It was a little long—he wanted to get in all of Mr. Jenkins's stories—but he kept the class interested, and Ms. Cunningham gave him an A.

After dinner that night, the Little League coach called. As usual, he was all business. "Bill," he said, "this is Coach Brown. I've got good news. You're in the majors."

"Great!" Bill blurted into the phone. "That's great! Thanks! Am I a pitcher?"

"You've got real promise as a pitcher," the coach said, "but you're a good catcher right now. The team needs a good catcher right now, so that's what I want you to be."

"Gee, thanks, Coach," Bill said. "Thanks! That's really great!"

"By the way," the coach added, "you'll be playing with Rob and Craig. They're on the team, too."

"Hey, Dad!" Bill called after he hung up the phone. "I made the team!"

He wanted to tell Mr. Jenkins, too. He knew Mr. Jenkins would be as glad as his father to hear the news. He couldn't wait to see Mr. Jenkins's face when he told him after school. A *double play*, Bill thought. I got an A, and I got on the team. I made a double play!

A phrase passed through Bill's mind as he thought of Mr. Jenkins. *"A stranger is a friend you've never met,"* the phrase went. Bill forgot where he first heard those words, but they certainly fit Mr. Jenkins.

The United States and Vietnam Today

The United States brought its last troops home from Vietnam in 1973. In 1975, the South Vietnamese army collapsed. North Vietnam united the country under a Communist government.

About fifteen years later, Vietnam reached out to the United States. It needed machinery to bring its factories up to date. It needed places to sell its products overseas.

Many Americans didn't want to help an old enemy. U.S. Senator John McCain disagreed with them. McCain was a Navy pilot during the war. The North Vietnamese shot down his plane in 1967 and kept him in prison until 1973. In the 1990s, he helped convince U.S. leaders like President Bill Clinton that closer ties with Vietnam would be good for both countries.

President Clinton with John McCain who was a fighter pilot during the Vietnam War. Today, he is a U.S. Senator. He believes that trade with the West will encourage Vietnam's Communist government to give its people more freedom.